A Note to Parents

DK READERS is a compelling programme for beginning readers, designed in conjunction with leading literacy experts, including Maureen Fernandes, B.Ed (Hons). Maureen has spent many years teaching literacy, both in the classroom and as a consultant in schools.

Beautiful illustrations and superb full-colour photographs combine with engaging, easy-to-read stories to offer a fresh approach to each subject in the series. Each DK READER is guaranteed to capture a child's interest while developing his or her reading skills, general knowledge, and love of reading.

The five levels of DK READERS are aimed at different reading abilities, enabling you to choose the books that are exactly right for your child:

Pre-level 1: Learning to read
Level 1: Beginning to read
Level 2: Beginning to read alone
Level 3: Reading alone
Level 4: Proficient readers

The "normal" age at which a child begins to read can be anywhere from three to eight years old. Adult participation through the lower levels is very helpful for providing encouragement, discussing storylines, and sounding out unfamiliar words.

No matter which level you select, you can be sure that you are helping your child learn to read, then read to learn!

LONDON, NEW YORK, MUNICH,
MELBOURNE, and DELHI

Editor Lisa Stock
Designer Carol Davis
Art Editor Toby Truphet
Managing Editor Laura Gilbert
Design Manager Maxine Pedliham
Publishing Manager Julie Ferris
Publishing Director Simon Beecroft
Pre-Production Producer Marc Staples
Reading Consultant Maureen Fernandes

For Lucasfilm
Executive Editor J.W. Rinzler
Art Director Troy Alders
Keeper of the Holocron Leland Chee
Director of Publishing Carol Roeder

First published in Great Britain in 2013 by
Dorling Kindersley Limited,
80 Strand, London, WC2R 0RL

13 14 15 16 10 9 8 7 6 5 4 3 2 1

001-187440-Nov/13

A CIP record for this book is available
from the British Library.

ISBN: 978-1-40936-535-8

Colour reproduction by Altaimage, UK
Printed and bound by L-Rex Printing Co., Ltd, China

Discover more at
www.dk.com

Contents

DK READERS

STAR WARS™

EVEN DROIDS NEED FRIENDS

Written by Simon Beecroft

The *Star Wars* galaxy
is a place where great
adventures happen.

Along the way, great friendships are made as well.

Some friends
make a
great team.

Anakin
Skywalker
is fearless.

Obi-Wan
Kenobi
is very wise.

Together
they are
unbeatable.

Some friends love
doing the same things.

Han Solo and
Chewbacca both love
flying spaceships.

Spaceships

Some friends don't like each other at first.

Luke thinks Han is a show-off.

Han thinks Luke is just a child.

But soon they become best friends.

Some friends have the same enemies.

Stormtroopers

Princess Leia and
Wicket both want
to defeat the
stormtroopers.

Some friends argue a lot.

Best friends R2-D2 and C-3PO argue almost all of the time!

Some friends have
known each other for
a long time.

Anakin is nine years old
when he meets Padmé.

She is fourteen.

Some friends have their ups and downs.

Lando Calrissian
tricks Han, but they
become friends again.

Some friends are
double trouble.

Dr Evazan and
Ponda Baba are
the worst bullies
you have ever seen!

Some friends don't know that they want to be friends.

Princess Leia and Han Solo pretend they don't like each other.

But really they love each other!

Some friends look
different from
each other.

Yoda is small
and green.

Chewbacca
is tall and
hairy.

Some friends look alike.

Logray and Chief
Chirpa are both Ewoks.

Ewoks

Some friends never let each other down.

These two Jedi look
after each other
in battle.

Who would you most like to be friends with?

Who are you less likely to be friends with?

Glossary

Ewok
A small, furry creature that lives in the forest on the planet of Endor.

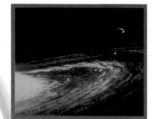

Galaxy
A group of millions of stars and planets.

Jedi
A member of a group with special powers that fights evil.

Stormtrooper
A soldier of an evil army who wears white armour.